Contents

What you need to know about the National Tests

KEY STAGE 2 NATIONAL TESTS: HOW THEY WORK

Pupils between the ages of 7 and 11 (Years 3–6) cover Key Stage 2 of the National Curriculum. In May of their final year of Key Stage 2 (Year 6), all pupils take written National Curriculum Statutory Tests in English, Mathematics and Science. The tests are carried out in school, under the supervision of teachers, but are marked by examiners outside the school.

The tests help to show what children have learned in these key subjects during Key Stage 2. They also help parents and teachers to know whether children are reaching the standards set out in the National Curriculum.

Each child will probably spend around five hours, in total, sitting the tests during one week in May. Most children will do two papers in Science and three papers in Mathematics and English.

The school sends the papers away to external examiners for marking. The school will then report the results of the tests to you by the end of July, along with the results of assessments made by teachers in the classroom, based on your child's work throughout Key Stage 2. You will also receive a summary of the results for all pupils at the school, and for pupils nationally. This will help you to compare the performance of your child with that of other children of the same age. The report from your child's school will explain to you what the results show about your child's progress, strengths, particular achievements and targets for development. It may also explain how to follow up the results with your child's teachers.

In addition, the publication of LEA primary school performance (or "league") tables will show how your child's school has performed in the teacher assessments and tests, compared to other schools locally.

UNDERSTANDING YOUR CHILD'S LEVEL OF ACHIEVEMENT

The National Curriculum divides standards for performance in each subject into a number of levels, from one to eight. On average, children are expected to advance one level for every two years they are at school. By Year 6 (the end of Key Stage 2), your child should be at Level 4. The table on page iii shows how your child is expected to progress through the levels at ages 7, 11 and 14 (the end of Key Stages 1, 2 and 3).

Most children will take three papers for Levels 3–5 in English. The Reading and Writing Tests will each be one hour long, and the Spelling and Handwriting Test will be 15 minutes long. An Extension Paper with Level 6 questions is available for exceptionally able pupils. This paper takes one hour.

What you need to know about the National Tests

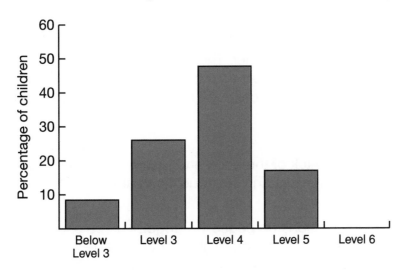

	7 years	11 years	14 years
Level 8+			☐ Exceptional
Level 8			
Level 7			
Level 6			
Level 5			
Level 4			
Level 3			
Level 2			
Level 1			

Exceptional performance

Exceeded targets for age group

Achieved targets for age group

Working towards targets for age group

How your child should progress

This book concentrates on Levels 3–5, giving plenty of practice to help your child achieve the best level possible. There are also some Level 6 questions for very able pupils. Do not worry if your child cannot do the Level 6 test; remember that Level 4 is the target level for children at the end of Key Stage 2. However, you may wish to discuss some of the Level 6 questions with your child (see page v). The bar chart below shows you what percentage of pupils nationally reached each of the levels in the 1998 tests for English.

Levels achieved in English, 1998

Although the results of all reading, spelling and mathematics tests will be reported in terms of a subject level, these test scores will also be converted into an age-standardised score, to show the school how your child's score in these tests compares with that of his or her age group. In addition, you will receive your child's reading and writing levels.

Preparing and practising for the English Test

ENGLISH AT KEY STAGE 2

The questions in this book will test your child on the Key Stage 2 curriculum for English. For assessment purposes, the National Curriculum divides English into three sections, called Attainment Targets (ATs). The first AT, Speaking and Listening, is assessed only by the teacher in the classroom, not in the written tests. The other two ATs are Reading (AT2) and Writing, including Spelling and Handwriting (AT3).

The National Curriculum describes levels of performance for each of the three English ATs. These AT levels are taken together to give an overall level for English. In addition, the test papers will assess both reading and writing and these levels will be reported to you.

USING THIS BOOK TO HELP YOUR CHILD PREPARE

This book contains four basic features:

Questions:	four test papers for Levels 3–5, in Reading, Writing, Spelling and Handwriting, and one extension paper for Level 6
Answers:	showing acceptable responses and marks
Notes to Parent:	giving advice on how to help your child avoid common mistakes and improve his or her score
Level Charts:	showing you how to interpret your child's marks to arrive at a level for each test and overall

SETTING THE TESTS AT HOME

Try setting the Reading Test first, mark it to see how your child has done and work through the answers and advice together. Then set the Writing, Spelling and Handwriting Tests on different days. Let your child carry out the tests in a place where he or she is comfortable. Your child will need a pen or pencil and a rubber may be used.

Setting the Reading Test

Detach pages 1–8 from the back of the book and fasten the pages together to make the English Booklet. The Reading Test questions are all on the theme of dolphins.

Read through the test instructions on pages 1–2 together. You should allow your child 15 minutes to read the booklet. You might want to suggest reading "Arion and the Dolphin" on pages 1–4 first, but emphasise that your child is not expected to *memorise* the readings; he or she may refer to the booklet at any time during the test.

Note the starting time in the box at the top of the test. After 45 minutes, ask your child to stop writing. If he or she has not finished, but wishes to continue working on the test, draw a line to show how much has been completed within the test time. Then let your child work to the end of the test, but check that he or she is able to cope with the questions as they become more difficult.

Preparing and practising for the English Test

Setting the Writing Test

To set the Writing Test, make sure your child has some writing paper. Read through the instructions on page 14 together. Once he or she has chosen one of the starting points for the Writing Test, you should allow your child 15 minutes to plan his or her writing. Then note the starting time on the top of the first sheet of writing paper. After 45 minutes, ask your child to stop writing.

Setting the Spelling and Handwriting Tests

The Spelling Test requires you to detach page 41 and read out a story to your child. Your child will be asked to fill in the missing words on his or her version of the story on pages 18–19. The test should take about 10 minutes. The Handwriting Test asks your child to copy out a passage on page 20 in his or her best joined-up handwriting. The Handwriting Test should take 5 minutes.

Setting the Level 6 Test

The Level 6 Test is an Extension Paper, designed to assess the Reading and Writing of exceptionally able children. Your child should only attempt to take the Level 6 Test if the results of the Levels 3–5 Tests suggest that he or she is working at the higher end of Level 5 in *both* the Reading and Writing Tests. If you decide that the test is too difficult for your child, you may still make use of the material by working through the test orally. Detach pages 7–16 from the back of the book and fasten the pages together to make the Level 6 Booklet. Read the story "Teeth" and the article on Anita Roddick in the booklet and discuss how these passages are written. This could be an opportunity to extend your child's awareness of character, plot and the way authors use words and language. You could also use the questions in this test as starting points for discussing a particular aspect of the story or article.

MARKING THE QUESTIONS

When your child has completed a test, turn to the Answers section at the back of the book. Work through the answers with your child, using the Notes to Parent to help give advice, correct mistakes and explain problems. If your child required extra time to complete a test, go through all the questions with your child, but do not include the marks for the "extra" questions in the total scores.

You can help your child if he or she tends to work slowly to use time more effectively:

- identify specific amounts of time needed to complete sections of a test, e.g. 15 minutes in the Writing Test to write an introduction;

- if your child is struggling with a question, ask him or her to read it through aloud, then ask if your child knows what the question means – this often helps clarify whether or not he or she can respond to the question;

- encourage your child to move on to the next question if he or she gets really stuck;

- identify areas of the Reading Test where the questions are easier – usually, the beginning of each section, e.g. pages 3 and 8.

Preparing and practising for the English Test

Using the recommended answers, award your child the appropriate mark or marks for each question. In the margin of each test page, there are small boxes divided in half. The marks available for each question are at the bottom; write your child's score in the top half of the box.

Enter the total number of marks for each section on the Marking Grid on page 50. This will enable you to calculate your child's Reading, Writing and English test level. Then add them up to find the total for the test. Look at the charts on page 49 to determine your child's level for each test, as well as an overall level.

FINALLY, AS THE TESTS DRAW NEAR

In the days before the tests, make sure your child is as relaxed and confident as possible. You can help by:

- ensuring your child knows what test papers he or she will be doing;

- working through practice questions, and discussing which answers are right and why.

Although the National Tests are important, your child's achievement throughout the school year is equally important. Encourage your child to do his or her best without putting him or her under too much pressure. Many children find that they enjoy doing tests, but it is natural that some may be nervous. Look out for signs of anxiety, such as changes in eating or sleeping habits, and reassure your child if he or she is worried about these tests.

Reading Test

Instructions

Carefully detach pages 1–6 from the back of this book. Fasten the pages together to make your own English Booklet. The questions in this reading test are about the dolphins in your booklet. The test is divided into four parts: "Arion and the Dolphin" (a Greek legend), "Astronomy and Ancient Civilisations" (an informative passage about constellations including the constellation Delphinus), "The Song of the Dolphin" (a poem) and a profile of a writer, Felice Arena, whose first book was about a boy and a dolphin.

You will have 15 minutes to read your booklet before you begin the test. You may wish to start reading "Arion and the Dolphin" first. Don't worry if you do not finish reading the whole section. You may look at the booklet as often as you wish during the test.

The written part of this test should take about 45 minutes.

Read all the words in the test carefully.

Some questions will ask you to fill in spaces in a sentence, for example:

> ### The title of the poem is ....

Some questions only require a word or phrase as an answer and have a short space or line, for example:

> ### Write down which day comes after Monday.

  ....

Some questions ask for an answer which is a bit longer. To answer these questions, you will be given two or three lines, for example:

> ### What do you enjoy doing at weekends?

  ....

....

Some questions ask you to fill in charts, for example:

What do you like doing...	Monday	Tuesday
at school?		
at home?		

Some questions require a long answer. These questions often ask you to give reasons for your answer, or to use the text in the English Booklet to help you to explain why you have a particular opinion. These questions will have a box for you to show your answer, for example:

Do you think that *Astronomy and Ancient Civilisations* in the English Booklet is interesting?

  Yes ☐ No ☐

Explain your opinion as fully as you can in the box below.

You might like to include details about

- whether the information on astronomy was interesting
- whether there was enough detail about ancient civilisations
- whether you are interested in astronomy.

....

....

....

....

Start [   ]   Finish [   ]

Dolphins

These questions are about the legend of *Arion and the Dolphin*.

1

> At the beginning of the story Arion was travelling to
> ……………………………………… . He had just won a prize of
> …………………….……………… in a music competition.

2
Q1

2

> Find a clue in the first paragraph (on page 1) that
> suggests that this story is not set in the present day.

……………………………………………………………………

1
Q2

3 i

> *...his playing, it is said, had charmed even the birds...*
> Why do you think the author included this detail?

……………………………………………………………………

……………………………………………………………………

1
Q3i

ii

> Can you find a similar idea later in the story?

……………………………………………………………………

……………………………………………………………………

1
Q3ii

4

> **Did Arion get on well with his parents?**

Yes ☐   No ☐

> **Find three pieces of evidence from the story to support your opinion.**

....

....

....

....

....

....

3
Q4

5

> ***...he drew his finger silently across his throat from ear to ear** (page 2).*
> **What does this tell you about the ringleader's plans?**

....

....

....

....

1
Q5

4

6   Arion, Theo and Philos had different attitudes to money.

In the chart below summarise each of these characters' attitude to money.

Character	Attitude to money
Arion	It wasn't important to him
Theo	
Philos	

7   *Theo bit his lip. Surely Arion didn't think the men would simply let him go?* (page 3)

Do you think that Theo was a coward not to protect Arion from the crew?

....

....

....

....

....

....

....

8   The legend of "Arion and the Dolphin" has been printed without any pictures. Imagine the publisher wants to include four pictures to show the main events of this story.

> **Write down the instructions for the artist so that they include the correct setting, characters and a main event in each picture. The first one has been done for you. Describe the next three pictures that follow the events in the story. Make sure you get the instructions for your pictures in the right order.**

Picture 1	Picture 2
Setting/background	Setting/background
A theatre in Corinth.	....
Characters	Characters
Arion and an audience.	....
Main event	Main event
The audience clapping and cheering.	....
....	....
Picture 3	**Picture 4**
Setting/background	Setting/background
....	....
Characters	Characters
....	....
Main event	Main event
....	....
....	....

3

Q8

9

Did you enjoy the story of *Arion and the Dolphin*?
Explain your opinion as fully as you can in the box below.

You might like to include details about
- the events in the story
- the characters
- your opinion of legends.

....

....

....

....

....

....

....

....

3

Q9

These questions are about *Astronomy and Ancient Civilisations*. Turn to page 4 of your reading booklet.

1

> **Studying the stars helped people in Ancient Greece. Looking at page 4, write down two ways in which studying the stars helped people in ancient times.**

....

....

2
Q1

2

> **Explain how most constellations got their names in Ancient Greece. Give one example.**

....

....

....

2
Q2

3

> **Has *Astronomy and Ancient Civilisations* been written to persuade, to inform or to entertain the reader?**

....

1
Q3

4

> **The text contains very few adjectives.**
> **Why do you think this is?**

....

....

1
Q4

8

5

Complete this glossary.

Glossary	
Ursa Major	Great Bear
Ursa Minor	
	Northern part of planet Earth
Astronomy	
Constellation	

4
Q5

6

The version of the legend of Arion given in this text differs slightly from that in the narrative version *Arion and the Dolphin*. What is the main difference?

....

....

....

....

1
Q6

These questions are about *The Song of the Dolphin*.

1

> **Where is the dolphin the "lord"?**

1
Q1

....

2 *...who found their final rest
trapped in the tangled terror
of the fisherman's nets?*

> **What do the last three lines tell us about what has
> happened to the dolphin's friends?**

1
Q2

....

....

3 *Dolphin
More liquid than the water.*

(i)

> **The poet uses this comparison to help him describe the
> dolphin. Find and copy one other comparison he uses.**

1
Q3i

....

....

(ii)

> **Do you think this is an effective comparison?**

Yes ☐   No ☐

Explain.

....

....

4   The poet uses alliteration (where the same sound is repeated, or several words begin with the same letter) throughout the poem, for example: *Fluent fluid swimmer*.

i

Find two other examples of alliteration.

....

....

ii

Which one do you prefer? Explain your opinion.

....

....

....

5   *...you're the only sea mammal*
    with a fishy sense of humour...

Why does the poet say that the dolphin has a sense of humour?

....

....

6   *...does the salt water wash your eyes?*

> **This line could refer to two different things.**
> **What are they?**

2
Q6

....

....

These questions are about *Profile of a Writer*.
See page 6 in your booklet.

1

> **Felice Arena says that the numbers of dolphins found in**
> **the North Sea and English Channel are declining.**
> **He gives reasons for this.**
> **Write down two of them in your own words.**

2
Q1

....

....

2   i

> **What does the writer of the *Factfile* want you to think**
> **about Felice Arena?**

1
Q2i

....

....

....

....

ii

> **How can you tell what the writer of the *Factfile* wants you to think about Felice Arena?**

✏️ ....

....

....

2
Q2ii

3

> **The *Factfile* and the back cover both give information about Felice, but the presentation of the back cover is different from that in the *Factfile*.**
> **Give one way in which it is different.**

✏️ ....

....

2
Q3

4

> **How does the description of the story *Dolphin Boy Blue* (on the back cover) try to make you think the book is worth reading? Find three words or phrases that make it sound attractive.**

✏️ ....

....

....

3
Q4

Writing Test

Instructions

Make sure your parent has read the notes on page v before you begin this writing test. Then read the instructions below.

On pages 15–17 there are four starting points for the writing test.
Read through all the starting points with your parent.
Choose **one** starting point to work on for the test.

Write down the number and title of the starting point you have chosen:

Planning

Your parent will give you one or two sheets of paper for you to note ideas about what you are going to write.

If you are planning to write story **1** or **2**, think about:

- how to start your story in an interesting way;
- getting into the story quickly;
- making sure the order of events is clear;
- including only a small number of characters;
- planning a good ending.

If you are planning to write a letter (number **3**) try to think about:

- what you are writing and why;
- organising your ideas so that they make sense to the reader;
- giving some details and explanations to make the writing interesting;
- planning a good ending.

If you are planning to write about your ambitions (number **4**) use the web to help you think about:

- the ambitions that you want to write about;
- the order in which you are going to write about each of your ambitions;
- the detail that you are going to include as you write about each ambition;
- planning a good ending.

You will have 15 minutes to plan your writing. Remember that planning should help you to get your ideas for your writing in order. You will not be marked on your plan. Try to write your ideas quickly; you do not have to use full sentences.

The test

Next, your parent will give you some more paper. Write your name and the title of your writing at the top of the first sheet.

You will have 45 minutes to do your writing.

CHOOSE ONE QUESTION ONLY.

1 Swim for your life!

> **Write a short story with the title *Swim for your life!***

You can write any story that fits the title. For example, it could be about swimming out of danger, learning to swim, a swimming contest... You can write about people, animals or even creatures from another world!

2 The sound of music

> ***It was only a song, but that song made all the difference.*
> Write a short story, using this idea to help you.**

You should think about

- what the song was like

- who sang it

- how the story began

- why the song made a difference.

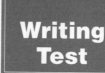
3 **Time for a change**

If tuna fish are caught in nets, there is a high risk that dolphins will also be caught and killed. Many tins of tuna have a label that says they are "dolphin friendly". Here is an example:

> Our tuna are caught with a pole and line,
> so avoiding danger to other marine life.

Some supermarkets sell tins of tuna that do not carry this label.

> **Write a letter of protest to the manager of one of these supermarkets.**

You should

- explain why you are concerned
- tell them why they should sell "dolphin friendly" tuna
- say what you will do if they do not change.

4   ## Ambition

> **What would you like to be when you grow up?**
> **What would you like to do?**

A "Profile of a Writer" told us about some of Felice Arena's ambitions. Two of his ambitions are to be an actor and a writer, but he has other ambitions as well.

Tell us all about your plans and dreams for the future.

Remember to explain why you hope for these things.

You can make up some details if you like!

This "web" may help you with your planning.

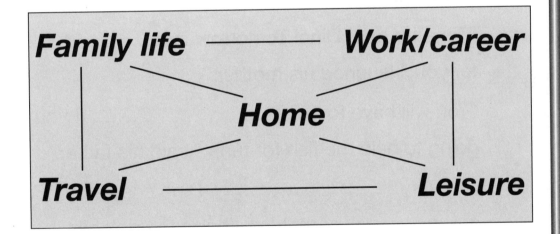

Family life —————— *Work/career*

Home

Travel —————— *Leisure*

35
Writing
Test

Spelling Test

Instructions

This Spelling Test will take about 10 minutes.

Your parent will read the story called "Fishing!" on page 41 out loud twice. You will follow along with your version of the story below, which has some words missing.

As your parent reads the story out loud for the first time, follow along with your version, but do not write anything. Then your parent will read the story for the second time.

When you come to a gap, wait for your parent to read you the word. Write the missing word on the line. If you are not sure how to spell the word, just try to write the letters you think are correct.

Fishing!

"Time for bed, Dino! Tomorrow is a .... day for you," laughed his mother.

"You will have to be up .... if you are going to help me fish for tuna," said his father.

"It's very ....," Dino cried, "but, Father, I am .... that I will harm the dolphins".

"I can understand that," his father ....

Dino continued, "Whales, dolphins, porpoises and seals are amongst the .... popular creatures who live in our seas". His father nodded in .... and his mother added, "They are .... mammals and they will need our help if they are to thrive in the next .... ".

"Don't worry Dino," his father said .... , "I might be a .... fisherman, but I also do my best not to harm other marine life. I'll show you tomorrow. Off to bed with you now – there's a long .... ahead of you!"

Next .... , Dino hurried to the boat with his father. It was .... in the small harbour as the .... of the fishing boats started up. Once out at sea, Dino's father began to talk about dolphins again. "I am sorry to say that I used to fish for tuna using drift nets," his father said. "They are dreadful nets," he continued sadly, "because not only do they .... tuna, but whales, dolphins and turtles get .... in them as well. I came to realise that I was .... of fishing for tuna without doing so much harm. Now I use a pole and line."

Dino smiled with ....

"Dino, we must get to work! We need to look out for a large school of dolphins because it .... means that tuna are close by. The dolphins tell me where I should fish!"

Total

10
Spelling
Test

Handwriting Test

Instructions

Write out the passage below very neatly in your own handwriting. Remember to join your letters if you can.

You have 5 minutes to do this test.

Dolphins!

Down through the ages many stories have been told about dolphins helping human beings. Young dolphins are very playful and they enjoy leaping out of the water. Dolphins will often swim alongside boats because they enjoy riding the bow-wave. By nature, dolphins are sociable, curious creatures and one of the wonders of planet Earth.

Write the passage on these lines.

....

....

....

....

....

....

....

Level 6 Test

Instructions

Before you start, think about how you are going to use your time during the test. You will have 60 minutes to do this test. This includes the time you have to read pages 7–16 of the Level 6 Booklet.

The questions in the test are based on the story "Teeth" on pages 7–12 and the article about Anita Roddick on pages 13–16 of the booklet.

You should try to answer each question as fully as you can. When a question asks you to explain your reasons, or to use examples from the story or passage, you should remember to do this.

Try to have a watch or clock nearby so that you can check that you are not spending too much time on one question or section of the test.

You should allow at least 25 minutes to work on the last question, which asks you to do some writing.

Before you start the last question, you should spend about 5 minutes planning your writing.

Ask your parent for some writing paper for the last question.

Start		Finish	

Questions about the story *Teeth* by Jan Mark.

1

> Re-read the opening paragraph. Do you think it is an effective beginning? In your answer, refer to both the content and the way it is written.

....

....

....

....

....

2

> What is the narrator's opinion of Eric Donnelly?
> Give examples from the text to justify your answer.

....

....

....

....

....

3

How does Jan Mark create humour in the story?
In your answer you should refer to the way the story is written, including:
• the language (choice of words and phrases, sentence structures)
• the events
• the way the story is organised.

....

....

....

....

....

....

....

....

....

....

....

Questions about the extract from *Body and Soul* by Anita Roddick.

4

> **When Anita Roddick started out, her methods were new and unusual.**
> **In what way does she say she was different from other people who were selling cosmetics?**

....

....

....

5 In paragraph 8 Anita Roddick writes
What I have learned is that it is better to share than to give or to receive.

> **Explain what you think she means by this sentence and how it relates to the way she lives her life.**

....

....

....

....

....

Questions about both extracts.

6   *Teeth,* by Jan Mark, is a fictional account of how Eric Donnelly set up a successful business. The extract from *Body and Soul* is Anita Roddick's own account of setting up a real business.

> **How does this affect the way the two pieces are written? Comment on the content, the way the texts are organised and the language choices.**

....

....

....

....

....

....

....

....

....

....

7   You are asked to write an article for your local newspaper on an unusual and successful business person. As Eric Donnelly and Anita Roddick are both visiting your town, you decided to write an article about **one** of them.

Write a report of their visit to your town, including an interview in which you explore how their individual approach to business has made them successful.

In this question remember to think very carefully about the quality of your writing.

Answers

HOW TO MARK THE READING TEST

Re-read the "Dolphins!" English Booklet (pages 1–6) before marking your child's answers to the Reading Test. This will help to clarify the marking scheme and will also help you to judge whether the content of an answer is correct. Different children have different ways of wording a correct answer; you need to judge whether your child "had the right idea".

Arion and the Dolphin   *Pages 1–4*

1   his home *or* Thessaly   *1 mark*
      fifty gold coins   *1 mark*

2   he was crowned with laurel leaves
      (accept "played a harp" as the modern equivalent might be a guitar)   *1 mark*

3   **i**   to show how beautifully he sang *or* to make Arion seem magical   *1 mark*
      ii   Theo thinks that the fish seemed to appreciate the music
          or the dolphins circled the boat drawn by the music   *1 mark*

4   This type of question requires your child to give a personal response to his or her reading. Award one mark for each reason that is supported by reference to the text.

Yes responses

1 mark: example answers
Yes, they didn't mind him playing his music.

or Yes, on the boat he was thinking of going home.

2 marks: example answers
Yes, his mother told him to ignore the teasing of the other children. She knew that music was important to him. His father also understood.

or Yes, both his parents understood him and told him to continue to play no matter what other people thought.

3 marks: example answers
Yes, when he was small his mother understood that his music was beautiful, even if the other children were too young and jealous of him to understand. When he was older his father told him to continue no matter what other people thought. He knew it was the only thing that made him happy.

or Yes, both his parents knew how important music was to him. They knew it was the only thing that would make him happy in life. When he won the 50 gold coins, Arion wanted to buy them a house of their dreams. At the end of the story he returns to their loving arms.

No responses

The text seems to support "yes" answers, but if your child can find reasons to support "no" answers, then mark them accordingly.

1 mark: example answers
No, his parents thought that he looked stupid playing music all the time.

or No, his parents thought, like everyone else, that he was wasting his time.

2 marks: example answers
No, all he wanted to do was to play music and his parents had to pretend he was good. He knew this because his mother was really on the side of the other children.

No, it says that he felt almost ashamed that playing the harp was all he wanted to do. He was afraid that his father really thought that he was useless.

3 Marks: examples

No, I don't think he really did get on with his parents. He must have wondered if his mother was only saying that he was talented. He felt guilty about not helping his father and knew that he really thought that he was useless. All the other people around him thought the same.

No, I think that Arion knew that he was really wasting his time. The other children told him and his mother was only being nice to him by saying that it wasn't true. He was also ashamed that his father knew him to be useless and was laughing at him. That is why they didn't go to the music festival with him. He only wanted to buy them a house to make it up to them.

5 He intended to kill Arion.   *1 mark*

6

Character	Attitude to money
Arion	It wasn't important to him
Theo	He liked money but he knew it was wrong to steal
Philos	He was prepared to kill to steal money

                                                                                    2 marks

7 Award one mark for yes/no response and a simple explanation.
Award two marks for yes/no response and a more detailed explanation.

1 mark: example answers

Yes, he was supposed to like Arion and he didn't really do anything to help him.

No, Theo was afraid of the other sailors and he also wanted Arion's money.

2 marks: example answers

Yes, he liked Arion and he knew it was wrong to steal from him and then kill him. He knew that the men would really kill Arion and he only stood by and bit his lip. He should have rushed to help him.

No, Theo had grown to like Arion because he was gentle and could charm the fish with his music. But he knew that if he tried to help Arion the other sailors would just kill him as well. He really couldn't help him at all.

8 Award 1 mark for each picture that has an appropriate description of a setting, identifies probable characters and describes the main event that the picture would illustrate.
To award 1 mark the setting, characters and main event must be completed for each picture.
Examples:

Picture 2
Setting: on board a ship
Characters: the crew with Philos and Theo
Main event: plotting to cut Arion's throat/steal his gold   *1 mark*

Picture 3
Setting: on board a ship
Characters: Arion, the crew, Theo and Philos
Main event: The crew surrounding Arion/Arion speaking to the crew trying to convince
             them not to kill him   *1 mark*

Picture 4
Setting: Overboard/in the sea
Characters: Arion, the dolphin (possibly Theo)
Main event: Arion riding across the waves on the back of a dolphin   *1 mark*

9 This type of question requires your child to give a personal response to his or her reading. Refer to the *Note to parent* for further guidance in marking this type of question. Generally, 1 mark for each reason that is supported by reference to the text.

1 mark: example answers

Yes, it was good, I like adventure stories.

Yes, I really like this sort of story. I wish I could see the dolphin.

No, it wasn't very exciting. I didn't believe in it at all.

No, it was boring, and its ending was really stupid.

2 marks: example answers

Yes, I like stories that have interesting characters and good endings. I really liked Arion and I was glad the dolphin saved him. When I look at the stars I will think about the ship and the pirates.

Yes, legends are really exciting, they are a bit like history. It told me how dangerous it was to travel in those days. I was glad that he won the money and that he was saved from the pirates by a dolphin.

No, I don't like legends. They are so unbelievable. Arion sounded a bit weak and he should have fought to save his money. The dolphin saving him is not very likely.

No, it was very short. You didn't really get to know any of the characters. Arion's parents were just too nice. I think that Theo could have helped him if he had wanted to. The bit where he went into the sea and didn't drown wasn't very believable.

3 marks: example answers

Yes, I thought that the action was very well presented. It started so peacefully with Arion's parents being so kind. Then he won his prize and was so happy to be going home to show people how good he was. It was a real shock that the sailors were going to kill him. Just when I thought that it was going to be the end of Arion he was clever and jumped into the sea. The rescue by the dolphin was lovely.

Yes, the legend makes you think of ancient times. I can see him happy at home, crowed in laurel after winning the competition, and then the awful events on the ship when all the sailors, with except Theo, wanted to kill him. The rescue by the dolphin was very dramatic. It makes sense of the names of the stars. They are always there to remind us of Arion's story.

No, legends are just untrue. It was very thoughtless of his parents to let him travel to Corinth alone. He should have taken more care to hide his money and then the sailors would not have had a reason to rob him. I don't think that the dolphin would really rescue him. He also returned home poor, which was his own fault.

No, the story didn't really tell you anything, except that some stars had been named after the dolphin. Arion was a bit stupid and had no common sense. I don't believe that his music could charm birds and fish. It was easy to see that he would be saved. His parents were too nice and the sailors too horrible. Most of the story was a bit childish.

Arion and the Dolphin Total 19 marks

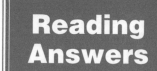

Note to parent

Your child is asked to respond to questions in a lot of different ways. Make sure that he or she understands how to answer questions that involve filling in charts or large boxes. If this is a problem talk it through until your child sees how the question works.

The questions look at the text from a range of different perspectives. If your child has difficulty with a particular type of question, try to identify the main point of the question and talk that aspect through with your child. Sometimes there is more than one aspect to a question but mainly they are as follows:

- Factual, e.g. question 1
- Overview of the story, e.g. question 8
- Deduction (sometimes using evidence from the text to support answer), e.g. questions 2, 4, 5, 6.
- Commenting on characters – why they said or did particular things, e.g. question 6.
- Identifying how words have been used in the text/how the author has used language, e.g. questions 2 and 3.
- Personal response or opinion (which is often linked to questions involving an overview of the story), e.g. questions 4, 7, 9.

Marking questions that require a personal or extended response:

Award 1 mark where your child has given a very basic answer with little supporting textual evidence.

Award 2 marks where your child has given a fuller answer with more detail drawn from the text, but has not demonstrated a complete response to the question.

Award 3 marks where your child has given a full answer and their own opinion is well supported by reference to the text.

It is not expected that your child will give exactly the same answers as those given in these answers or include the same details. However, the answers given should match the demands of the examples for an award of 1, 2 or 3 marks.

If your child has difficulty with the questions that require a longer response discuss two or three ideas that your child might include in the answer and also identify the vocabulary he or she might find useful. Get your child to "say" his or her answer before trying to write it.

Astronomy and Ancient Civilisations   *Pages 4–5*

1   helped them to find their way across land or sea at night   *1 mark*
helped them to predict the pattern of weather or seasons   *1 mark*

2   they got their names from characters or creatures in Greek legends   *1 mark*
An additional mark for an example of a constellation,
e.g. the Delphinus constellation got its name from the legend of Arion and the Dolphin.   *1 mark*

3   to inform   *1 mark*

4   it is an information text /it is not a story   *1 mark*

5

Glossary	
Ursa Major	**Great Bear**
Ursa Minor	Little Bear
Northern hemisphere	**Northern part of planet Earth**
Astronomy	The study of stars
Constellation	A group of stars

4 marks

6   In "Arion and the Dolphin', Arion jumped overboard to get away from the crew.
This text says that the crew threw Arion into the water.   *1 mark*

Astronomy and Ancient Civilisations Total 11 marks

Note to parent

Only a small number of questions in this section directly involve factual recall, such as questions 1 and 6. Most questions are drawing on your child's awareness of an information text (questions 3 and 4) or his or her awareness of how words are used (questions 4 and 5). If your child finds this section difficult you may wish to read other information texts and discuss the way the text is written and the way words are used.

The Song of the Dolphin   **Page 5**

1   in the sea   *1 mark*

2   They died *because* they became trapped in fishing nets.
(*Only credit answers which link the dolphin deaths to being trapped.*)   *1 mark*

3 **i**   with muscles like blue-grey steel   *1 mark*
   ii *1 mark: example answers*
      Yes, it makes you think of the colour and strength of a dolphin swimming.

      No, steel is far stronger than a dolphin. If they were that strong they wouldn't get caught in nets.

      2 marks: example answers
      Yes, in the water the dolphins are grey with a blue sheen. They are muscular creatures that are strong just like steel is.

      No, dolphins are a dark grey so I don't think it is a good comparison of colour.

      I also don't think the comparison with steel is good because dolphins seem quite weak to me.   *Up to 2 marks*

4 **i**   *Accept any two of the following:*
      dip and dive
      dive down deep
      deep, deep, too deep for tears
      sing sad songs
      trapped in the tangled terror   *Up to 2 marks*

   ii   *Examples of preferences:*

      dip and dive or *dive down deep*
      1 mark: example answers
      It makes you think of swimming in the water and diving.

      or It just sounds wrong, dolphins don't dip in water.

      2 marks: example answers
      It makes you think of a dolphin skimming the top of the ocean then diving deep, deep down.

      or It doesn't make the sound of a dolphin swimming. It sounds too jerky. Then it sounds like the dolphin has vanished.

dive down deep or *deep, deep, too deep for tears*

1 mark: example answers
It makes you think about the dolphin going deep into the ocean, to find a safe place.

or The dolphin wouldn't really be able to go so deep into the ocean.

2 marks: example answers
The poet makes it sound as though the dolphin is leaving our world to go to a secret sad place where it can be on its own, away from us.

or The dolphin can't really get away from the nets of the fisherman. For the dolphin there is no place that is too deep for tears.

sing sad songs or *trapped in tangled terror*

1 mark: example answers
It makes you feel sad for all the dolphins caught in nets.

or Dolphins can't really sing songs about their friends caught in nets.

2 marks: example answers
The poet makes the words sound like the singing of dolphins as they mourn their friends caught in nets.

or Dolphins can't sing those sorts of songs and the nets sound all caught up which means they can't hold a dolphin.

5   Credit any response that indicates that the poet is making reference to the
    dolphin's physical appearance which makes it appear that it is laughing.   *1 mark*

6   Seawater is salt water that washes the dolphin's eyes.   *1 mark*
    Tears wash the dolphin's eyes and they are salt water too.   *1 mark*

The Song of the Dolphin Total 12 marks

Note to parent

To answer these questions your child needs to read the text quite closely. Questions 1, 2 and 6 involve deducing meaning from particular lines of the poem. If your child finds these questions difficult discuss the meaning of the particular lines concerned. Question 4 involves your child in being able to recognise alliteration. If he or she finds this question difficult you may wish to find other examples of rhyme and alliteration in poems that your child knows well. The most challenging questions involve personal response (question 3 (ii) and 4(iii)). The guidance given above on open response questions is applicable here as well.

A Profile of a Writer   Page 6

1   *Accept any two of the following answers:*
    The sea is polluted.
    Dolphins get tangled in nets.
    There are fewer fish.
    1 mark for each correct answer   *Up to 2 marks*

2   i   Credit answers that indicate that the writer wants the reader to
         to think that Felice Arena is very talented or successful.   *1 mark*
    ii   Credit answers that show an awareness that the writer uses phrases
         to highlight his abilities e.g "endless talents",

     or he acts in "daunting" parts,
     or he played the part of a "gorgeous" person.
     Award 1 mark for two reasons, 2 marks for three or more reasons.   *Up to 2 marks*

3 *Accept the following:*
     The use of headings;
     or The use of notes rather than complete sentences.
     Award 1 mark for each response.   *Up to 2 marks*

4 *Accept any three of the following:*
     Heart-stopping story
     Sparkling blue waters
     Take on the world and win
     … a very special relationship
     Can he sustain his winning streak?
     Award 1 mark for each response.   *Up to 3 marks*
     A Profile of a Writer Total 10 marks

Note to parent

In all four questions your child has to identify information or deduce meaning from the text. Question 2 (ii) focuses on the use of language.

Enter the total marks scored on each section of the Reading Test on the Marking Grid on page 50. Then turn to page 49 to determine your child's level for Reading.

Writing Answers

HOW TO MARK THE WRITING TEST

Before you mark your child's writing, read it through at least twice so that you become familiar with it. There are two marking keys. Use the key on pages 35–36 if your child wrote a story. Use the key on pages 37–38 if your child wrote a letter, or about his or her ambitions. The key will ask you questions about how your child's writing is written and organised, what style of writing is used and how punctuation is used.

After you have read the instructions below on how to use the marking key, read the example on pages 39–40 to see how Jonathan's story was marked using the key for stories.

Begin with the "Just below Level 3" questions for "How is the story/letter written and organised?". Tick the "yes" or "no" box for each question at this level. Then go on to consider the questions for each level in this section in turn. You may find that you do not answer "yes" to all the questions for one level. When this happens, look at how you answered the questions for the level below and the level above – which level has the most "yes" answers? Decide which level best describes how your child's writing is written and organised. Enter the number of marks for that level on the Marking Grid on page 50.

Next, answer the questions for "What style of writing is used?" in the same way. These questions ask you to consider the vocabulary your child has used and how sentences have been constructed. Decide which level best describes your child's writing style and enter the number of marks for that level on the Marking Grid on page 50.

Do the same for "How is punctuation used?" These questions ask you to evaluate your child's use of capital letters, full stops, question marks, etc. Decide on the level that best describes your child's punctuation and enter the number of marks for that level on the Marking Grid on page 50.

The marks from the Writing Test, along with the scores from the Spelling and Handwriting Tests, will contribute to your child's overall level for Writing (see page 49).

Note to parent

You may notice that your child's level for "style" is different from his or her level for "organisation" or "punctuation". It is possible to achieve different levels for these different categories.

The marking keys show what is needed to achieve each level. By analysing your child's writing in such detail, you will be able to see what he or she does well and where the writing needs to develop. When your child is planning other writing, discuss how he or she could take account of particular features from the marking key. For example, if you notice that the events are disjointed and do not relate well in the story your child wrote for this test, you might discuss how the events could link together sensibly when your child plans another story.

Writing
Answers

MARKING KEY: STORIES

How is the story written and organised?	Yes	No

JUST BELOW LEVEL 3

Does the writing include details about two or more events (real or imagined)? ☐ ☐
Does the story have more than one character? ☐ ☐
Does it have the basic elements of a story (an opening and some events)? ☐ ☐
Does it rely on simple story words (e.g. *one day... suddenly... the end*) to show it is a story? ☐ ☐
Award 9 marks if this level best describes your child's written organisation.

LEVEL 3

Does the story relate to the title? ☐ ☐
Are there some interesting details (suspense, humour, description)? ☐ ☐
Are the settings or the thoughts or feelings of the characters described? ☐ ☐
Are there several connected events that follow each other? ☐ ☐
Does the story feel as though it has been written with a reader in mind? ☐ ☐
Does the story have a simple ending? ☐ ☐
Award 12 marks if this level best describes your child's written organisation.

LEVEL 4

Does the story have a suitable opening? ☐ ☐
Does the story have a clear beginning, middle and end? ☐ ☐
Are the events of the story sensibly related with a reader in mind? ☐ ☐
Do the characters make a contribution to the story? ☐ ☐
Is there significant interaction between the characters? ☐ ☐
Is there some development of the characters, through what they say or do? ☐ ☐
Does the ending relate convincingly to the main events (e.g. not just "we all went home")? ☐ ☐
Award 15 marks if this level best describes your child's written organisation.

LEVEL 5

Is the writing well organised and well paced overall? ☐ ☐
Are there any interesting story devices, for example:
• does it start with dialogue? ☐ ☐
• does it start in the middle of a dramatic event? ☐ ☐
• does it move between times and places? ☐ ☐
• does it include a sub-plot? ☐ ☐
• does it end with a twist in the story? ☐ ☐
Is the reader's interest engaged and sustained? ☐ ☐
Are events, dialogue and description skilfully interwoven? ☐ ☐
Does the writer express a personal point of view, for example by:
• commenting on characters and events? ☐ ☐
• giving an idea of characters" thoughts and feelings? ☐ ☐
Is there some use of paragraphs to mark the beginning, main events and end? ☐ ☐
Does the ending relate convincingly to the central plot? ☐ ☐
Is it a convincing story type (e.g. mystery, true-life, myth)? ☐ ☐
Award 18 marks if this level best describes your child's written organisation.

HIGH LEVEL 5

Does the story show development of a theme (controlling idea) as well as a plot? ☐ ☐
Is it written convincingly, in appropriate paragraphs, and with confidence? ☐ ☐
Does it fully engage and sustain the reader's interest? ☐ ☐
Does it include relationships or conflict between the characters? ☐ ☐
Award 21 marks if this level best describes your child's written organisation.

Writing Answers

What style of writing is used?	Yes	No
JUST BELOW LEVEL 3 Are many of the ideas linked by "and" or "and so" or "and then"?	☐	☐
Is simple vocabulary used (e.g. "make", "get", "thing")?	☐	☐
Award 2 marks if this level best describes your child's writing style.		
LEVEL 3 Are simple descriptive phrases used (e.g. "a sunny day")?	☐	☐
Are joining words such as "but" or "because" used?	☐	☐
Are simple adverbs used (e.g. "quickly", "slowly")	☐	☐
Is the basic grammatical structure of sentences correct (e.g. subject and verb agreement)?	☐	☐
Award 4 marks if this level best describes your child's writing style.		
LEVEL 4 Is the vocabulary interesting and lively?	☐	☐
Are complex sentences used (e.g. phrases joined by "so that", "although", "if")?	☐	☐
Are descriptive phrases used (e.g. "as fast as his legs could carry him")?	☐	☐
Overall, is the writing interesting with most tenses used consistently?	☐	☐
Award 5 marks if this level best describes your child's writing style.		
LEVEL 5 Is the language vivid and interesting and does it give the intended meaning?	☐	☐
Is there a mixture of simple and complex sentences?	☐	☐
Is Standard English used (or colloquialism and dialect for effect)?	☐	☐
Award 6 marks if this level best describes your child's writing style.		
HIGH LEVEL 5 Is the style completely appropriate and effective?	☐	☐
Is there a suitable range of vocabulary and sentence length?	☐	☐
Is alliteration used (e.g. "a lone laser beam lashed the side of the ship")?	☐	☐
Is imagery used (e.g. "city lights twinkled and danced below them")?	☐	☐
Award 7 marks if this level best describes your child's writing style.		

How is punctuation used?	Yes	No
JUST BELOW LEVEL 3 Are capital letters and full stops used correctly in some places?	☐	☐
Award 2 marks if this level best describes your child's punctuation.		
LEVEL 3 Are capital letters and full stops used correctly in half the sentences?	☐	☐
Award 4 marks if this level best describes your child's punctuation.		
LEVEL 4 Are capital letters, full stops and question marks used correctly in most cases?	☐	☐
Is there punctuation within sentences (e.g. commas, speech marks, apostrophes)?	☐	☐
Award 5 marks if this level best describes your child's punctuation.		
LEVEL 5 Are capital letters, full stops and question marks used correctly in almost all cases?	☐	☐
Is punctuation within sentences used correctly in most cases?	☐	☐
Award 6 marks if this level best describes your child's punctuation.		
HIGH LEVEL 5 Is all punctuation accurate?	☐	☐
Is a wide range of punctuation used?	☐	☐
Does punctuation help to vary the pace of the writing (e.g. are sentences varied in length)?	☐	☐
Award 7 marks if this level best describes your child's punctuation.		

MARKING KEY: LETTER AND INFORMATION WRITING

How is the letter or information written and organised?	Yes	No

JUST BELOW LEVEL 3

Does the writing contain a series of statements? ☐ ☐

Is there some sign of attempts to organise the writing (e.g. an opening, a concluding statement)? ☐ ☐

Are the points made either very brief or over-long? ☐ ☐

Award 9 marks if this level best describes your child's written organisation.

LEVEL 3

Does the writing have a simple introduction? ☐ ☐

Does the writing include a number of linked statements? ☐ ☐

Is the writing related to the topic? ☐ ☐

Does the writing contain information described in some detail to add interest? ☐ ☐

Does the writing have a simple ending? ☐ ☐

Award 12 marks if this level best describes your child's written organisation.

LEVEL 4

Does the writing have a suitable introduction or opening? ☐ ☐

Is the information presented in a way that a reader can follow? ☐ ☐

Are suitable formats used (e.g. "Dear..." for a letter, sections or headings for an article)? ☐ ☐

Are the main points/aspects of information covered? ☐ ☐

Is there a reasonable amount of detail? ☐ ☐

Is there a suitable final sentence? ☐ ☐

Overall, is the writing interesting? ☐ ☐

Award 15 marks if this level best describes your child's written organisation.

LEVEL 5

Is the writing well organised and well paced overall? ☐ ☐

Does the opening make clear the purpose of the writing? ☐ ☐

Is the reader's interest engaged and sustained? ☐ ☐

Is the level of formality generally appropriate? ☐ ☐

Are the main issues covered? ☐ ☐

Are individual points adequately covered? ☐ ☐

Are individual points sensibly organised and linked? ☐ ☐

Award 18 marks if this level best describes your child's written organisation.

HIGH LEVEL 5

Is the piece really well written? ☐ ☐

Are points relevant and well organised? ☐ ☐

Is the level of detail appropriate and balanced? ☐ ☐

Is there a strong introduction and conclusion? ☐ ☐

Does the writer express his or her views with authority? ☐ ☐

Are ideas organised into paragraphs to mark introduction, middle and conclusion? ☐ ☐

Award 21 marks if this level best describes your child's written organisation.

Writing Answers

What style of writing is used?	Yes	No

JUST BELOW LEVEL 3

Are sentences simple, like speech (e.g. many sentences starting "there is")? ☐ ☐
Are many sentences linked by "and" or "then" or "but"? ☐ ☐
Is vocabulary simple (e.g. "make", "get", "do")? ☐ ☐
Award 2 marks if this level best describes your child's writing style.

LEVEL 3

Does it show an awareness of the intended reader by using appropriate vocabulary? ☐ ☐
Are simple descriptive phrases used (e.g. "a long holiday")? ☐ ☐
Are joining words such as "but" or "because" used? ☐ ☐
Are simple adverbs used (e.g. "quickly", "badly")? ☐ ☐
Award 4 marks if this level best describes your child's writing style.

LEVEL 4

Is the vocabulary precise and varied (with suitable technical words used)? ☐ ☐
Are complex sentences used (e.g. phrases joined by "so that", "although", "if")? ☐ ☐
Are phrases used to clarify meaning (e.g. "a dear little cottage in the middle of the woods")? ☐ ☐
Award 5 marks if this level best describes your child's writing style.

LEVEL 5

Is the language precise, using technical and specific words where needed? ☐ ☐
Is there a mixture of simple and complex sentences? ☐ ☐
Award 6 marks if this level best describes your child's writing style.

HIGH LEVEL 5

Is the style completely appropriate and effective including the level of formality? ☐ ☐
Is there a subtle variety of vocabulary and sentence lengths? ☐ ☐
Is word order changed for effect (e.g. "Unless you change things without delay, these beautiful creatures will die out." instead of, "These beautiful creatures will die out unless you change things now.")? ☐ ☐
Award 7 marks if this level best describes your child's writing style.

How is punctuation used?	Yes	No

JUST BELOW LEVEL 3

Is there some use of capital letters and full stops? ☐ ☐
Award 2 marks if this level best describes your child's punctuation.

LEVEL 3

Are capital letters and full stops used correctly in half the sentences? ☐ ☐
Award 4 marks if this level best describes your child's punctuation.

LEVEL 4

Are capital letters, full stops and question marks used correctly in most cases? ☐ ☐
Is there punctuation within sentences (e.g. commas, speech marks, apostrophes)? ☐ ☐
Award 5 marks if this level best describes your child's punctuation.

LEVEL 5

Are capital letters, full stops and question marks used correctly in almost all cases? ☐ ☐
Is punctuation within sentences used correctly in most cases? ☐ ☐
Award 6 marks if this level best describes your child's punctuation.

HIGH LEVEL 5

Is all punctuation accurate? ☐ ☐
Is a wide range of punctuation used? ☐ ☐
Does punctuation help to vary the pace of the writing (i.e. are sentences or phrases of varied length)? ☐ ☐
Award 7 marks if this level best describes your child's punctuation.

USING THE MARKING KEY: AN EXAMPLE

Ambition

I have chosen the careers below because they are things I am intrested in at the moment and I would like to do in my later life. I hope to achieve these ambitions by hard work.

The first out of two things I would like to do is join the R.A.F before I go to college so they will sponser me through college. In college I hope to to study in great depth : physics, aerodynamics, graphics and techolgy. I would like to study these so that when I leave college I will resign from the R.A.F and make a living by desiging areoplanes and computer games and sell them off to big companies.

My second choise is to go to college and study biology and chemistry and become a chemist who tries to make cures for deadly diseases.

When I come out of college I will stay with my parents until I earn enough money to buy a house. I hope to have a house in Scotland either in Edinburg or Glasgow. I whish to have a house there for three main reasons though there are other smaller reasons. The three main reasons are as follows'. one: Scotland has fresh air and I am asmatic so fresh air is a great help, two: It has fresh water which is healthier than hard water and three: It has lots of spare ground so if I take on ambition one but also buy a plane I can fly round a lovely unspoilt contryside and get no bumps from the exoust of car engin or power stations.

If I have any more spare time I would enjoy flying a plane if possible or go cycling or visit a museam, read or play on the computer and if I felt brave enough go mountain climbing.

I will do my best to follow these ambitions but they are a long way off and things might change so for now I will continue with my ambitions for the near future which are to pass the S.A.T.S with a level 4 and gain the Duke of Edinburg and genurily do my best at school work.

HOW IS THE STORY WRITTEN AND ORGANISED?

Jonathan has started with an appropriately formal introduction to his writing, setting it out in a separate paragraph. He sounds a personal note and engages the reader's interest by mentioning the "hard work" that will be needed. The writing is well organised, with clear "signposts" for the reader (e.g. "The first... My second choice... When I come out of college...") and paragraphs are used to group ideas appropriately. The level of coverage is suitable: he includes enough detail to create interest, dealing in turn with key areas indicated by the starting point, and creating links between sections by referring back to the ideas he has already mentioned. His ending is well-judged, reflecting the ideas expressed in the introduction – that these are his current ambitions, and that he is prepared to work hard to achieve them. The organisation of the piece shows features of Level 5. Nevertheless, the purpose of the writing might be unclear to anyone who had not read the starting point, although the title does help the reader to work out the context of the piece. Overall, the piece is on the borderline between Levels 4 and 5, and 15 marks should be awarded.

WHAT STYLE OF WRITING IS USED?

Jonathan's use of vocabulary is generally good, and he includes a number of technical words (e.g. sponsor, aerodynamics, design, diseases, exhaust), as well as a range of adjectives, adverbs and phrases to clarify meaning (e.g. deadly diseases; enough money to buy a house; lovely unspoilt countryside). His spelling is sometimes uncertain, but spelling is not a consideration here. The piece contains a range of sentence structures, and Jonathan's ability to handle complex sentences is shown by such examples as: "become a chemist who tries to make cures; I would enjoy flying a plane; and, if I felt brave enough, go mountain climbing". There are some slightly awkward expressions ("The first out of two things ... other smaller reasons"), but the style overall is characteristic of Level 5, so 6 marks should be awarded.

HOW IS PUNCTUATION USED?

Capital letters and full stops are used correctly in most cases, and Jonathan makes largely appropriate use of colons. He uses commas to separate items in a list ("visit a museum, read..."), but does not use them to separate clauses, and this sometimes creates difficulties for the reader (e.g. "and if I felt brave enough go mountain climbing"). Punctuation is best described as Level 4, so 5 marks should be awarded.

HELPING JONATHAN TO DEVELOP HIS WRITING

Overall, Jonathan scores 26 marks (Level 4) for his writing test. The organisation of his writing was very close to Level 5, so he would bring his level up by practising writing introductions that set the context of the piece very clearly. He was given a lower mark for punctuation, so this is an area where he could be given help, particularly in the appropriate use of commas.

He has some problems with accuracy in spelling, although he is generally able to make a sensible guess (e.g. "sponsur"). His writing might benefit by checking for accuracy. If he re-reads the work carefully, he may well notice the occasions where he has missed a letter (e.g. "engin, grond"), and if he imagines reading the piece aloud this will help him to notice where commas are needed to indicate a pause.

Parent's guide to the spelling test

Your child's version of the Spelling Test is printed on pages 18–19. Your child has to write down the missing words in his or her version as you read the story aloud. The full text of the story is printed below and you may detach this page. The words printed in **bold italics** are the words your child will have to spell.

Go through the instructions on page 18 together. Read the story the first time without stopping. Then read it a second time, pausing in the appropriate places to allow your child to write down the missing words in his or her version.

STORY TO READ ALOUD

Fishing!

"Time for bed, Dino! Tomorrow is a ***special*** day for you," laughed his mother.

"You will have to be up ***early*** if you are going to help me fish for tuna," said his father.

"It's very ***exciting***," Dino cried, "but, Father, I am ***worried*** that I will harm the dolphins."

"I can understand that," his father ***replied***.

Dino continued, "Whales, dolphins, porpoises and seals are amongst the ***most*** popular creatures who live in our seas". His father nodded in ***agreement*** and his mother added, "They are ***fascinating*** mammals and they will need our help if they are to thrive in the next ***century***".

"Don't worry Dino," his father said ***quietly***, "I might be a ***successful*** fisherman, but I also do my best not to harm other marine life. I'll show you tomorrow. Off to bed with you now – there's a long ***journey*** ahead of you!"

Next ***morning***, Dino hurried to the boat with his father. It was ***noisy*** in the small harbour as the ***engines*** of the fishing boats started up. Once out at sea, Dino's father began to talk about dolphins again. "I am sorry to say that I used to fish for tuna using drift nets," his father said. "They are dreadful nets," he continued sadly, "because not only do they ***catch*** tuna, but whales, dolphins and turtles get ***trapped*** in them as well. I came to realise that I was ***capable*** of fishing for tuna without doing so much harm. Now I use a pole and line." Dino smiled with ***relief***.

"Dino, we must get to work! We need to look out for a large school of dolphins because it ***usually*** means that tuna are close by. The dolphins tell me where I should fish!"

HOW TO MARK THE SPELLING TEST

After the test, total up the number of words your child has spelled correctly. This total for the Spelling Test is converted into marks which contribute to the overall level for Writing. Enter the marks from this test on the Marking Grid on page 50. Marks should be given as indicated on the next page.

Number of correct words	Marks	Number of correct words	Marks
1–2	1	11–12	6
3–4	2	13–14	7
5–6	3	15–16	8
7–8	4	17–18	9
9–10	5	19–20	10

IMPROVING YOUR CHILD'S SPELLING AT KEY STAGE 2

During Key Stage 2 your child should develop his or her skills in spelling. The Literacy Strategy sets out words that children should learn each year they are in primary school. You could check that your child knows the Year 5 and 6 spelling list. Spelling is best learnt when both phonic strategies (sound) and visual strategies (recognising groups of letters) are used.

In the early stages of learning to spell, children should learn to memorise short common words, e.g. *get, went*. Then they should learn to match sounds to letters – this should help them to spell simple words.

As your child becomes more aware of the relationship between sounds and letters, you should help him or her to see that patterns exist. These include:
* the effect of doubling the vowel, e.g. "ee" as in *sheep, sleep, freeze*
* how certain vowels and consonants combine, e.g. "ar" as in *car, card, hard*
* how some consonants combine to make particular sounds, e.g. "ch" as in *chain, choice, chase*
* how a silent "e" affects a vowel, e.g. *hop/hope, bit/bite, car/care*
* how two vowels combine to give a particular sound, e.g. "oi" as in *oil, boil, toil*
* how the grouping of two or more letters gives a particular sound, e.g. "igh" as in *sigh, high, slight*
* how words that have long vowel sounds such as *journey* need to be committed to the visual memory
* how words with double consonants need to be memorised, e.g. *successful*.

Your child should also develop a visual sense of how words "look", and consider letter sequences in more complex words. Your child needs to get used to considering whether a word "looks right".

A useful way to help your child to memorise a spelling is to use the routine of "Look, Cover, Write, Check":

Look at a word and identify phonic patterns or sequences of letters within the word.

Cover the word, but try to memorise the spelling.

Write the spelling down.

Check whether the written word is spelt correctly, identify any mistakes, and then try again.

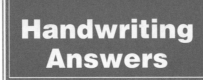

HOW TO MARK THE HANDWRITING TEST

When your child has completed the Handwriting Test, consider the questions below to decide which mark should be awarded. Sometimes you will not be able to answer "yes" to all the questions in a particular section, but overall you should feel that one set of questions comes closest to describing your child's handwriting. Enter the number of marks for this test on the Marking Grid on page 50. Then turn to page 49 to determine your child's levels in Writing and overall in English.

Handwriting style	Yes	No	Marks
Can you read the handwriting? Are the size and shape of some letters irregular? Is the spacing between letters and words irregular?	☐ ☐ ☐	☐ ☐ ☐	1 mark
Are most letters formed correctly? Are most letters of similar size (such as h, k, l and g, y, p) the *right* size? Is the spacing between most letters and words regular?	☐ ☐ ☐	☐ ☐ ☐	2 marks
Are letters the right size most of the time? Are some letters and words written in a joined style? Is the spacing between letters and words appropriate?	☐ ☐ ☐	☐ ☐ ☐	3 marks
Are the letters the right size all of the time? Is all the handwriting joined? Can the joined handwriting be read? Is the handwriting joined correctly? Is the spacing between letters and words even?	☐ ☐ ☐ ☐ ☐	☐ ☐ ☐ ☐ ☐	4 marks
Is the writing joined and legible throughout the whole writing test? Is the joined handwriting fluent (i.e. do the letter joins seem to "flow" evenly)? Is the writing completed in a style that is consistent and confident?	☐ ☐ ☐	☐ ☐ ☐	5 marks

A sample Handwriting Test is marked on page 44.

USING THE MARKING KEY: AN EXAMPLE

> # Dolphins
>
> Down through the ages many stories have been told about dolphins helping human beings. Young dolphins are very playful and they enjoy leaping out of the water. Dolphins will often swim alongside boats because they enjoy riding the bow - wave. By nature, dolphins are sociable, curious creatures and one of the wonders of Planet Earth.

MARKING KELLY'S HANDWRITING

Kelly has made a number of spelling mistakes as she copied out the handwriting passage, but this does not affect her mark for handwriting. If your child has made spelling mistakes in this test, you should not deduct marks. After you have awarded the appropriate marks for the handwriting test, discuss the spelling mistakes separately.

Kelly's handwriting is joined and easy to read, and the spacing between words is mainly even. There are a number of instances, however, where Kelly's letters are not the correct size. For example "often" the "t" is too tall and the "f" is too small above the line – the "f" above the line and the "t" should be the same size. The "s" at the beginning of "stories", "swim" and "sociable" is slightly too large although it is usually the correct size in the middle and at the end of words. For this reason, Kelly should be awarded 3 marks, since 4 marks requires correct letter size throughout the test.

With a little guided practice focusing on correct letter sizes, Kelly would soon achieve a higher score since she is developing a confident style.

HOW TO MARK THE LEVEL 6 TEST

To mark this test, you will need to make judgements about the *quality* of your child's answers. This means that answers will not simply be "correct" or "incorrect" but you will be awarding marks on the basis of your child's ability to interpret the texts.

1   The first paragraph sets the scene for the story – the narrator and Eric grew up together. The pun on "roots" and the tone of voice prepare the reader for the jokes and sardonic tone of the text as a whole.

Award 1 mark for a partial description of the content of the paragraph

Eric and the narrator grew up in the same town.

Award a second mark for a partial evaluation of the content *and* a comment about the way the paragraph is written, mentioning either the pun on "roots" or an evaluation of the tone of the narrator and the effect this has (e.g. "That's a good one" prepares the reader for a more critical view of Eric).

Award a third mark for a description of the content *and* a full evaluation of language, e.g. the use of the pun on "roots" and why that is so amusing, and the effect of the tone of the narrator in preparing the reader for the sardonic tone of the text.

2   **Award 1 mark** if your child recognises the main idea: that the narrator dislikes Eric Donnelly as he thinks that he is, for example, crafty and flashy.

Award 2 marks where the points your child makes are supported by direct references to the text.

3   **Up to 3 marks** can be awarded for this question. Marks should be given as follows:

Award 1 mark for explanations that identify how humour is developed through language, for example the choice of words (including puns); the use of language (e.g. the repetition of the phrase "as far as it goes"); the marked variation in the length of sentences used and how this is effective (e.g. "Roots" is a pun and a one-word sentence).

Award 1 mark if your child explains how the ordering of events contributes to the humour in the story.

Award 1 mark if your child can discuss how devices the author uses contribute to the humour in the story, e.g. the use of a narrator, the ordering of events and "flashbacks".

4   **Award 1 mark** if your child describes three of the unusual things Anita Roddick did to draw people into her shop:
*   she sprayed strawberry essence on the pavement
*   she put out old-fashioned sandwich boards
*   she got local art students to make posters
*   she drenched the front of the shop with exotic perfume oils
*   she hung branches of dried flowers from the ceiling
*   she put out pot-pourri.

Award 2 marks if, in addition to identifying three of the above points, your child also notes that Anita Roddick's attitudes to her customers were unusual, e.g. she rubbed shoulders with her customers in order to sell her products; she wasn't a business person first and foremost; she knew that many people could not afford a lot of money for cosmetics so she sold small quantities in small packages.

5 **Award 1 mark** for an explanation that she feels that you can learn more about people if you share ideas with them.

Award a second mark for identifying that Anita believes that sharing can provide opportunities for people to help themselves.

Award a third mark if the answer also explains that Anita believes that it is possible to share ideas from around the world and by this type of sharing it is possible to contribute to sustainable growth in poorer countries.

6 **Award 1 mark** for answers that comment on the contrasts between the presentations of the content, e.g. that the story is humorous whereas the biography is mainly serious.

Award a second mark for recognising the ways in which stories and biographies differ. Answers should comment on how the texts are organised, e.g. the chronological organisation in the biography compared with the "flashback" structure of the story.

Award a third mark for answers that comment on the differences in language used, e.g. speech-like structures in the story as though the narrator is speaking to the reader directly, contrasted with the formal structures and tone of the biography. The biography uses technical language (e.g. "rapidly expanding company") whereas the story uses puns and short phrases to promote humour.

7 This question requires your child to do some extended writing. Use the marking key on pages 47–8 to mark this question in the same way as you marked your child's Levels 3–5 Writing Test. Enter your child's marks for organisation, for grammar and punctuation, and for spelling and handwriting on the Marking Grid on page 50.   *16 marks*

Level 6 Total 32 marks

Level 6 Answers

MARKING KEY: LEVEL 6

How is the writing organised?	**Yes**	**No**

BELOW LEVEL 6

Is the piece really well written? ☐ ☐
Are points relevant and well organised? ☐ ☐
Is the level of detail appropriate and balanced? ☐ ☐
Is there a strong introduction and a strong conclusion? ☐ ☐
Are ideas developed in an interesting way? ☐ ☐
Are ideas or views expressed with authority? ☐ ☐
Are ideas appropriately organised into paragraphs? ☐ ☐
Is some information from the original texts used to support ideas and views? ☐ ☐
Award 4 marks if this level best describes your child's written organisation.

LEVEL 6

Is the piece really well written? ☐ ☐
Are points relevant and well organised? ☐ ☐
Is the level of detail appropriate and balanced *and* does it sustain the interest of the reader? ☐ ☐
Are devices used which show an awareness of the reader (e.g. by making clear that the writer is a journalist)? ☐ ☐
Are the main issues covered well with information from one of the texts being used? ☐ ☐
Are some of the ideas and structures from the original text used? ☐ ☐
Are ideas organised appropriately into paragraphs? ☐ ☐
Does the final paragraph conclude with an appropriate summary which is either factual or persuasive? ☐ ☐
Is the writing controlled and confident? ☐ ☐
Award 8 marks if this level best describes your child's written organisation.

How are grammar and punctuation used?	**Yes**	**No**

BELOW LEVEL 6

Is all punctuation accurate? ☐ ☐
Is a wide range of punctuation used? ☐ ☐
Does punctuation help to vary the pace of the writing (e.g. are sentences and phrases of varied length)? ☐ ☐
Is the style completely appropriate and effective, including the level of formality? ☐ ☐
Is there a subtle variety of vocabulary and sentence lengths? ☐ ☐
Is word order changed for effect? ☐ ☐
Are appropriate choices made between Standard English and slang? ☐ ☐
Award 2 marks if this level best describes your child's grammar and punctuation.

LEVEL 6

Is a wide range of punctuation used? ☐ ☐
Does the punctuation vary the pace of the writing and clarify meaning? ☐ ☐
Are commas used to show divisions between clauses? ☐ ☐
Are commas used to clarify meaning? ☐ ☐
Are colons, semi-colons or dashes used to clarify meaning? ☐ ☐
Is the style of writing appropriate for a published article? ☐ ☐
Is there an appropriate and sustained level of formality in the writing? ☐ ☐
Is there a mixture of short and long sentences that are used effectively? ☐ ☐
Is there variety in the vocabulary used (e.g. a varied use of verbs and adjectives)? ☐ ☐
Award 4 marks if this level best describes your child's grammar and punctuation.

How are spelling and handwriting used to present the writing?	Yes	No
BELOW LEVEL 6		
Is handwriting joined, fluent and easy to read?	☐	☐
Are words with regular complex patterns spelled correctly (e.g. "satisfied", "appearance", "apprehensive")?	☐	☐
Award 2 marks if this level best describes your child's spelling and handwriting.		
LEVEL 6		
Is handwriting joined, fluent and legible?	☐	☐
Is the writing style altered appropriately if the article requires any special features (e.g. sub-headings)?	☐	☐
Is spelling accurate, including the spelling of irregular words (e.g. "guarantee", "nuisance")?	☐	☐
Award 4 marks if this level best describes your child's spelling and handwriting.		

Determining your child's level

FINDING YOUR CHILD'S LEVEL IN READING AND WRITING

When you have marked your child's Reading Test, enter the marks scored for each section of the test on the Marking Grid overleaf. Then add them up.

Using this total for the Reading Test, look at the chart below to determine your child's level for Reading:

Reading

Below Level 3	Level 3	Level 4	Level 5	High Level 5
up to 10	11–22	23–35	36–45	46+

When you have marked your child's Writing, Spelling and Handwriting Tests, enter the marks scored for each section on the Marking Grid overleaf. Then add them up. Using this total for all three tests, look at the chart below to determine your child's overall level for Writing.

Writing (including Spelling and Handwriting)

Below Level 3	Level 3	Level 4	Level 5	High Level 5
up to 18	19–30	31–38	39–48	49+

FINDING YOUR CHILD'S OVERALL LEVEL IN ENGLISH

After you have worked out separate levels for Reading and Writing, add up your child's total marks. Use this total and the chart below to determine your child's overall level in English. The chart also shows you how your child's level in these tests compares with the target level for his or her age group.

Total for Reading and Writing

Below Level 3	Level 3	Level 4	Level 5	High Level 5
up to 29	30–53	54–74	75–94	95+
Working towards target level for age group		Working at target level	Working beyond target level	

In the Key Stage 2 English Test, Level 6 will not be awarded if Level 5 has not been achieved on the main tests for Reading, Writing and Spelling and Handwriting. If your child achieved a Level 5 in *both* Reading and Writing above, you may wish to set the Level 6 Test. Enter the marks scored for each section of the test on the Marking Grid overleaf. Then add them up. The chart below shows whether or not your child is working at Level 6.

Level 6 Test

Below Level 6	Level 6
up to 25	26+

Marking Grid

Reading   Pages 1–13

Section	Marks available	Marks scored
Arion and the Dolphin	19	
Astronomy and Ancient Civilisations	11	
Poem: The Song of the Dolphin	12	
A Profile of a Writer	10	
Total	**52**	

Writing   Pages 14–20

Section	Marks available	Marks scored
How is the story/letter written and organised?	21	
What style of writing is used?	7	
How is punctuation used?	7	
Spelling marks (see pages 41–42)	**10**	
Handwriting marks (see page 43)	**5**	
Total	**50**	

Level 6   Pages 21–26

Section	Marks available	Marks scored
Test questions 1–6	16	
Question 7: how is the writing organised?	8	
Question 7: how are grammar and punctuation used?	4	
Question 7: how are spelling and punctuation used to present the writing?	4	
Total	**32**	

ARION AND THE DOLPHIN

Arion was on stage, looking up at row upon row of admiring faces. His head was crowned with laurel leaves, and as he blew kisses to the crowd with his right hand he cradled, in his left, the harp that had made him the darling of the Corinth music contest. The whole theatre was filled with the sound of applause, deafening waves of clapping and cheering that died away to a whisper then swelled again, rising and falling, rising and falling...

Arion became aware that he was no longer on the stage, but in bed. Nevertheless he smiled, as he yawned and stretched, feeling the sea rise and fall beneath the boat. The contest was over and he was on his way home aboard the trading ship Sea Witch, but that moment of victory at Corinth would stay with him for the rest of his life.

The sound of the harp had delighted Arion ever since he could remember, and from the age of six he had spent his time playing and singing at every opportunity, despite the taunts of the other children in the village. His mother always told him to ignore them. "They're too young to appreciate your talents," she would say, or maybe, "They're just jealous."

One day his father had taken him aside and asked him about his ambitions in life, and Arion felt almost ashamed that he could think of nothing more useful than playing his beloved harp. "If it's music that you love," his father had smiled, "then stick to it, without worrying about what other people think." He patted his shoulder. "It's the only way to be really happy in life."

He had stuck to it, and his playing, it is said, had charmed even the birds round his quiet country home. Now, at sixteen, he had won the greatest music prize in the whole of Greece: a prize that brought honour and fame, and even (though for Arion this was the least important part) a rich prize of fifty gold coins.

For Arion, the money meant nothing, except perhaps that he could buy his parents the little house and farm of their dreams. Up on the

Dolphins!

deck of the Sea Witch, though, were seven sailors who felt very differently. Even as Arion was daydreaming, the crew were just a few feet above his head, plotting and scheming, and wondering how they could get their hands on the little purse of coins that hung from Arion's belt.

"Fifty coins," said Philos, the ringleader, "That would mean seven pieces of gold for each and every one of us. We needn't work again – at least not for a year or two!"

The youngest of the sailors, Theo, said nothing. He would like the money, of course, but he knew that to steal it would be wrong. Anyway, he had come to like this gentle musician, who day after day would play his harp out on deck simply for the pleasure of making music. Why, even the fish seemed to appreciate the notes that came from the harp, and more than once Theo had seen dolphins circling the boat, drawn by the magical songs!

"Excuse me," Theo interrupted, "Haven't you forgotten something? If we steal Arion's money, he'll report us to the authorities as soon as we go ashore, and we'll all be thrown into prison."

There was a roar of laughter, vicious and raucous, then a hush as Philos thrust his face into Theo's. "You don't think he'll be going ashore, do you?" he almost whispered, and with a grin he drew his finger silently across his throat from ear to ear.

There was a sudden clatter as the trap door leading up from the hold was pushed back and Arion emerged into the sunlight, harp trailing from his left hand. "Morning!" he shouted cheerfully, and sat himself down to play, unaware of the heavy silence, and the sideways glances of the sailors as they withdrew to their tasks.

This was the fourth day, the mid-point of the voyage, and the Sea Witch was surrounded by sparkling blue water as far as the eye could see. As Arion played and sang, a breeze filled the ship's sails, blowing her gently away from Corinth towards the shores of Thessaly and closer each moment to his own village. Arion's thoughts, so full until now of the excitement of the last few weeks, began to turn to his family. Without realising, he had begun to strike up a sad little song about a soldier who longs for home, and the feelings of the soldier were so close to his own that he sang more beautifully than ever before.

It was more than the sailors could bear. Arion was beginning to melt even their stony hearts, and if he continued playing like this they could never bring themselves to kill him. The ringleader crept forward, his knife at the ready, and with a nod of the head signalled the others to follow.

As the last note of the song died away, Arion sighed and looked up. At the sight of those seven pairs of eyes, and the glint of the sun on the polished blade, his mouth was suddenly dry and he heard the pounding of blood in his ears. He saw instantly the way things were, and that his life must surely be at an end. Yet he knew he must speak.

'Gentlemen," he began, in a hoarse, croaky voice that he scarcely recognised as his own. He paused and tried to hum softly to give himself courage. "Gentlemen," he began again, "I see that you have fallen under the spell of a sound far stronger than my voice. It is the clinking of gold coins that is music to your ears, and I and my harp can have no further use for you. But do not stain your hands with my blood, or reduce yourselves to the level of mere criminals."

Theo bit his lip. Surely Arion didn't think the men would simply let him go? There was no way the other sailors would spare his life once they had their hands on that purse, and even less hope that they would forget their greed and let him keep his money.

'Here!" shouted Arion, seizing the purse, "Take the gold and I'll take my chance in the sea!" And throwing the purse onto the deck, where the sailors shoved and scrambled to get hold of it, he jumped up, harp in hand, and leapt overboard.

Now, while the sailors scrambled and shoved to get their hands on the gold, only Theo ran to the rail to see what had become of Arion after he hit the water. A curious sight met his eyes. Arion, still clutching his harp, was skimming, as it seemed, over the surface of the water. In another moment, he was high above the waves, supported by a laughing dolphin. The dolphin had been lured by the golden tones of Arion's music, so dancing over the sea rather than swimming, it carried him gently home to Thessaly, to the loving arms of his family.

****

Nor is this the end of the story. When Arion came to shore, he did not forget his dolphin. He wrote a new song about the faithful creature that had saved his life and, many years later, when Arion and his dolphin had lived their lives to the full, there appeared in the sky a cluster of stars that have ever since been known as Delphinus, the Dolphin.

Reproduced with permission from the writer, Helena Ross.

Astronomy and Ancient Civilisations

Astronomy (literally, the science of naming the stars) was studied by many ancient civilisations. It was important in Babylon, in China, in Egypt and in Greece.

It is difficult for us to imagine these days what it must have been like to live at a time when there were no electric lights, no maps, compasses or other technology to help travellers find their way. Instead, people looked up to the stars at night, and studied the way stars are grouped and the way they "move" around the night sky.

Astronomy in Ancient Greece

The study of the stars was very important for practical reasons, enabling travellers to make their way over land and sea at night, and helping people to predict the pattern of seasons and weather. It was also linked to the Greek legends and stories that were handed down from generation to generation.

Often, groups of stars or constellations would have shapes that reminded astronomers of particular legends, and they would name the constellations after characters or creatures in the stories. The traditional names given by the Ancient Greeks were passed on to the

Ancient Romans, and many of these are still used by astronomers today. You may recognise the names of some of the larger constellations such as the Great Bear (Ursa Major) and Little Bear (Ursa Minor).

One of the less well-known constellations is Delphinus, the Dolphin, a small group of four stars seen in the sky of the northern part of the planet or the Northern Hemisphere. It was named by astronomers in Ancient Greece after the dolphin in the legend of Arion, the musician. According to the legend, Arion was rescued by the dolphin after being thrown overboard from a ship.

The Song of the Dolphin   **Paul Cosway**

Dolphin
  More liquid than the water
    through which you move,
As you perform your tricks how do you feel?
  Fluent fluid swimmer
    with muscles like blue-grey steel
     you seem to laugh and smile.
    Have you heard the rumour
  that you're the only sea mammal
with a fishy sense of humour?
In the depths of the sea
  you are a lord.
    What do you *really think*
  of the humans who applaud?
And as you dip and dive, dive down
  deep, deep, too deep for tears,
    does the salt water wash your eyes
     and remind you of your fears
      as you sing sad songs to lost dolphin loves
     who found their final rest
    trapped in the tangled terror
  of the fisherman's nets?

Dolphins!

A Profile of a Writer

Felice Arena published his first book "Dolphin Boy Blue" in 1996. To many people Felice is better known as Marco Alessi in the television serial *Neighbours*. This profile of Felice Arena looks at his career, his commitment to the conservation of whales and dolphins, and his first book.

Factfile:
Felice Arena

Age: Early twenties
Born: Victoria in sunny Australia
Now lives: London, England
Talents: Endless! He was a state swimming champion; played basketball for his school; can act, dance and sing; enjoys writing and painting; and even speaks fluent Italian!
Big break: Playing the role of gorgeous Marco in *Neighbours*.
Other claims to fame: Guest presenter on *Disney TV*; has appeared on *The Big Breakfast* and *Noel's House Party*; starred in tours of musicals *Godspell*, *What a Feeling* and *Hair*.
Most daunting roles: Playing in *Godspell* and appearing in *Hair*.
What he could have been: Your teacher! Felice is a trained schoolteacher.
What he wanted to be: An Olympic Gold Medallist.
What he's doing now: Writing! *Dolphin Boy Blue* was Felice's first novel. His second book for Collins is *Mission Buffalo* (published in August 1997).

As you may imagine, Australia's oceans are full of dolphins, but my first experience of swimming with a dolphin was off the coast of Israel. It was a lifetime dream come true. She even let me stroke her!

However, what is not so easily imagined is that dolphins can also be found in the UK. In fact, twenty-five species have been recorded in the North Sea and English Channel, but the numbers have depleted and they are under constant threat from pollution, entanglement in fishing nets, and reduction in fish stocks.

If you would like to know more about dolphins or whales, you can write to:

The Whale and Dolphin Conservation Society,
Alexander House,
James Street West,
Bath, Avon
BA1 5BT

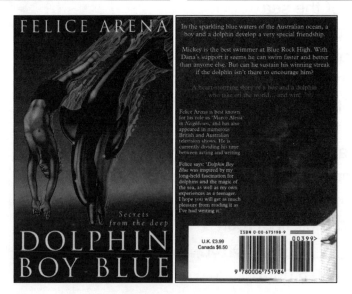

These extracts and cover are reproduced with permission from the publisher, HarperCollins*Publishers* Ltd and Christopher Little Agency.

Teeth

by Jan Mark

Eric still lives in the town where we grew up. He says he wants to stay close to his roots. That's a good one. You can say that again. Roots.

Some people are rich because they are famous. Some people are famous just for being rich. Eric Donnelly is one of the second sort, but I knew him before he was either, when we were at Victoria Road Primary together. I don't really *know* Eric any more, but I can read about him in the papers any time, same as you can. He was in one of the colour supplements last Sunday, with a photograph of his house all over a double-page spread. You need a double-page spread to take in Eric these days. He was being interviewed about the things he really considers important in life, which include, in the following order, world peace, conservation, foreign travel (to promote world peace, of course, not for *fun*), his samoyeds (a kind of very fluffy wolf) and his wife. He didn't mention money but anyone who has ever known Eric – for three years like I did or even for five minutes – knows that on Eric's list it comes at the top, way in front of world peace. In the photo he was standing with the wife and three of the samoyeds in front of the house, trying to look ordinary. To *prove* how ordinary he is he was explaining how he used to be very poor and clawed his way up using only his own initiative. Well, that's true as far as it goes: his own initiative and his own claws – and other people's teeth. He didn't mention the teeth.

"Well," says Eric modestly, in the Sunday supplement, "it's a standing joke, how I got started. Cast-iron baths." That too is true as far as it goes. When Eric was fifteen he got a job with one of those firms that specialize in house clearances. One day they cleared a warehouse which happened to contain two hundred and fifty Victorian cast-iron baths with claw feet. It occurred to Eric that there were a lot of people daft enough to actually *want* a Victorian bath

7

with claw feet; people, that is, who hadn't had to grow up with them, so he bought the lot at a knock-down price, did them up and flogged them. That bit's well known, but in the Sunday supplement he decided to come clean. He came clean about how he'd saved enough money to buy the baths in the first place by collecting scrap metal, cast-offs, old furniture and returnable bottles. "A kind of rag-and-bone man," said Eric, with the confidence of a tycoon who can afford to admit that he used to be a rag-and-bone man because he isn't one any more. He still didn't mention the teeth.

I first met Eric Donnelly in the Odeon cinema one Saturday morning during the kids" show. I'd seen him around at school before – he was in the year above mine – but here he was sitting next to me. I was trying to work out one of my front teeth which had been loose for ages and was now hanging by a thread. I could open and shut it, like a door, but it kept getting stuck and I'd panic in case it wouldn't go right side round again. In the middle of *Thunder Riders* it finally came unstuck and shot out. I just managed to field it and after having a quick look I shoved it in my pocket. Eric leaned over and said in my earhole, "What are you going to do with that, then?"

"Put it under me pillow," I said. "Me mum'll give me sixpence for it."

"Oh, the tooth fairy," said Eric. "Give it to us, then, I'll pay you sixpence."

"Do you collect them?" I asked him.

"Sort of," said Eric. "Go on – sixpence. What about it?"

"But me mum knows it's loose," I said.

"Sevenpence, then."

"She'll want to know where it went."

"Tell her you swallowed it," Eric said. "She won't care."

He was right, and I didn't care either, although I cared a lot about the extra penny. You might not believe this, but a penny – an old penny – was worth something then, that is, you noticed the difference between having it and not having it. Eric was already holding it out on his palm in the flickering darkness – one penny and two threepenny bits. I took them and gave him the tooth in a hurry – I didn't want to miss any more of *Thunder Riders*.

"Your tooth's gone, then," my mum said, when I came home and she saw the gap.

"I swallowed it," I said, looking sad. "Never mind," she said, and I could see she was relieved that the tooth fairy hadn't got to fork out another sixpence. I'd lost two teeth the week before.

It was half-term that weekend so I didn't see Eric till we were back at school on Wednesday. Yes, Wednesday. Half-terms were short, then, like everything else: trousers, money... He was round the back of the bog with Brian Ferris.

"Listen," Eric was saying, "threepence, then."

"Nah," said Brian, "I want to keep it."

"But you said your mum didn't believe in the tooth fairy," Eric persisted. "You been losing teeth for two years for *nothing*! If you let me have it you'll get threepence – *four*pence."

"I want it," said Brian. "I want to keep it in a box and watch it go rotten."

"Fivepence," said Eric.

"It's mine. I want it." Brian walked away and Eric retired defeated, but at dinner time I caught him at it again with Mary Arnold, over by the railings.

"How much does your tooth fairy give you?" he asked.

"A shilling," said Mary, smugly.

"No deal, then," Eric said, shrugging.

"But I'll let *you* have it for thixpenth," said Mary, and smiled coyly. She always was soft, that Mary.

I started to keep an eye on Eric after that, him and his collection. It wasn't *what* he was collecting that was strange, it was the fact that he was prepared to pay. I noticed several things. First, the size of the tooth had nothing to do with the amount that Eric would cough up. Also, that he would never go above elevenpence. That was his ceiling. No one ever got a shilling out of Eric Donnelly, even for a great big thing with roots.

Now Eric, although he was a year older, was smaller than me. That day I followed him home.

It was not easy to follow Eric home. They tended to marry early in that family so Eric not only had a full set of grandparents but also two great-grandmothers and enough aunties to upset the national average. Eric was always going to stay with one of them or another. He was heading for one of his great-grandmas that evening, along Jubilee Crescent. I nailed him down by the phone box.

"Listen, Donnelly," I said. "What are you doing with all them teeth?"

Give him credit, he didn't turn a hair. A lot of kids would have got scared, but not Eric. He just said, "You got one for me, then?"

"Well, no," I said, "but I might have by Saturday."

"Sevenpence?" said Eric, remembering the previous transaction, I suppose. He had a head for figures.

"Maybe," I said, "but I want to know what you do with them."

"What if I won't tell you?" Eric said.

"I'll knock all yours out," I suggested, so he told me. As I thought, it was all down to the grannies and aunties. They were sorry for poor little Eric – Dad out of work, and no pocket money. If he lost a tooth while he was staying with one of them he put it under the pillow and the tooth fairy paid up. There being two great-grannies, two grannies and seven aunties, it was hard for anyone to keep tabs on the number of teeth Eric lost and it hadn't taken him long to work out that if he didn't overdo things he could keep his eleven tooth fairies in business for years. Kids who didn't have a tooth fairy of their own were happy to flog him a fang for a penny. If he had to pay more than sixpence the tooth went to Great-Granny Ennis, who had more potatoes than the rest of them put together.

By the time that he was eleven I calculate that Eric Donnelly had lost one hundred teeth, which is approximately twice as many as most of us manage to lose in a lifetime. With the money he saved he bought a second-hand barrow and toured the streets touting for scrap, returnable bottles and so on, which was what earned him enough to buy the two hundred and fifty Victorian baths with claw feet which is the beginning of the public part of Eric's success story, where we came in. I suppose there is some justice in the fact that at thirty-eight Eric no longer has a single tooth he can call his own.

No – I am not Eric's dentist. I am his dustman. Occasionally I turn up just as Eric is leaving for a board meeting. He flashes his dentures at me in a nervous grin and I give him a cheery wave like honest dustmen are meant to do.

"Morning, Donnelly," I shout merrily. "Bought any good teeth lately?" He hates that.

Extract from the story "Teeth" by Jan Mark, adapted and reproduced with permission from *Hundreds and Hundreds*, edited by Peter Dickenson, Puffin, 1984.

Anita Roddick

The first branch of The Body Shop opened in Brighton in 1976. Twenty years later there were almost 1500 branches in over 40 countries. The Body Shop is concerned about the environment, the testing of cosmetics on animals, and the protection of human rights around the world. The company buys the ingredients for some of its products from people who live in the rainforest. This gives these people a way to feed their families. Anita Roddick founded The Body Shop – in this passage from "Body and Soul" she describes how it all started.

Brighton shopkeepers opening up for business in the spring of 1976 occasionally had cause to sniff the air, then pause and scratch their heads at the curious sight of this odd woman in dungarees with unruly dark hair walking down the street intently spraying strawberry essence onto the pavement. It was not a madwoman – it was me, laying a scented trail to the door of The Body Shop in the hope that potential customers would follow it.

Believe me, I was prepared to try anything in those early days to get customers into my shop. I wanted to get passers-by to stop, so I put big, old-fashioned sandwich boards outside and got local art students to make posters promoting one or another of the products. I drenched the front of the shop in the most exotic perfume oils so that it always smelled wonderful as you approached; inside I hung huge branches of dried flowers from the ceiling, and there was fragrant pot-pourri everywhere.

Once I had got people inside, it was all down to me. I never *sold* anything to anyone, at least not in the way that selling was then understood; it was not my style to be a pushy saleswoman. In the retail trade, sales staff tend to use counters as a refuge to avoid making contact with customers. That was not me: I was never behind the counter. I would be tidying a shelf next to someone and I would dab something like the Glycerine and Rosewater Lotion on the back of my hand and say: "Umm, I love the smell of this. Here, try it. What do you think?"

I didn't know anything about business when I opened the first Body Shop. The vocabulary of business was part of a language I did not speak. And I certainly had no ambitions to start a big international company. I didn't want to change the world; I just wanted to survive and be able to feed my kids. The extent of my business knowledge went no further than the grim knowledge that I would have to take in £300 a week to stay open. But I did know how to trade.

I started with a kind of grace which clung to the notion that in business you didn't tell lies. I didn't think of myself as an entrepreneur. My motivation for going into the cosmetics business was irritation: I was annoyed by the fact that you couldn't buy small sizes of everyday cosmetics and angry with myself that I was always too intimidated to go back and exchange something if I didn't like it. I also recognised that a lot of the money I was paying for a product was being spent on fancy packaging which I didn't want. So I opened a small shop to sell a small range of cosmetics made from natural ingredients in five different sizes in the cheapest possible plastic containers.

If it hadn't worked, I would have found something else to do. But it did work. And I am glad. Without my entirely understanding it, and certainly without my planning it, the shop seemed to appeal to lots of different kinds of customers – to students, young mothers, day trippers, foreign visitors. Even guys liked to come in and look around. Women of my Mum's age liked the notion of returnable

bottles, perhaps because it reminded them of those thrifty days during and after the war. It was classless, friendly and stylish; people felt comfortable even if they were only browsing.

Today, The Body Shop is an international company rapidly expanding around the world and in those intervening years I have learned a lot. I spend about five months every year travelling the world looking for new products, and I make sure everyone knows where I have been, whom I have met and what ideas have surfaced, whether it is paper-making in Nepal, or finding a use for brazil nuts in the Amazon.

Accompanied by an interpreter and sometimes an anthropologist, I am happy to go anywhere in the world to look for trade and to talk to women about what they use – and what their mothers and grandmothers used – to polish and cleanse and protect their skin. What I have learned is that it is better to *share* than to give or to receive. I have learned that the poorest people are anything but helpless when given the slightest opportunity to help themselves.

I have also learned the pure joy that is to be obtained from mixing with simple people whose lives are untainted by what we have laughably described as "progress".

During the late eighties and early nineties The Body Shop combined with Friends of the Earth, Survival International and Greenpeace to run joint campaigns on acid rain, recycling, the vanishing countryside, the ozone layer and the green consumer. Our staff achieved what no other environmental group internationally has ever achieved: in less than a month they collected more than one million signatures to protest against the burning of the rainforests. All we did was bring the issue to the marketplace and use our shops as a campaign platform. We donated window displays and provided posters and leaflets, and our staff and customers did the rest.

When people talk about The Body Shop they talk about our philosophy, our campaigning, our social and educational policies and the way we have managed to humanise business practices.

What everyone wants to know – and no one seems to be able to work out – is if there is a direct link between the company's values and its success. When people ask us how we do it I tell them it is easy.

First, you have to have fun.

Second, you have to put love where your labour is.

Third, you have to go in the opposite direction to everyone else.

I don't know how many of them understand what we are saying, but the fact is that we are still pretty lonely on our home territory. It's a great pity: personally I would go to the other end of the earth to learn from a company that was trying to make the world a better place.